Robin hood

LEVEL 4

Re-told by: Jocelyn Potter
Series Editor: Melanie Williams

Pearson Education Limited
Edinburgh Gate, Harlow,
Essex CM20 2JE, England
and Associated Companies throughout the world.

ISBN: 978-1-4082-8864-1

This edition first published by Pearson Education Ltd. 2013

7 9 10 8 6

Text copyright © Pearson Education Ltd. 2013
Copyright © 2013 Disney Enterprises, Inc. All rights reserved.

The moral rights of the author have been asserted
in accordance with the Copyright Designs and Patents Act 1988

Set in 17/21pt OT Fiendstar
Printed in China
SWTC/06

Published by Pearson Education Ltd

For a complete list of the titles available in the Pearson English Kids Readers series, please go to
www.pearsonenglishkidsreaders.com. Alternatively, write to your local Pearson Education office or to
Pearson English Readers Marketing Department, Pearson Education, Edinburgh Gate, Harlow, Essex CM202JE, England.

King Richard of England was away. His brother, John, took his place. Prince John wanted to be king – and he wanted money. Poor people became poorer.

Robin Hood hated Prince John. Robin and his friends robbed him and gave the money to the poor.

One day, Robin Hood and Little John were in Sherwood Forest. Suddenly, they heard a noise.

"Look! It's Prince John!" Robin shouted. "He's coming through the forest."

"He always carries a lot of money," Little John said. "This is going to be a good day for the poor people of Nottingham. But he has guards. Do you have a plan, Robin?"

"Yes," Robin said. "Let's find some women's clothes. We're going to be fortune-tellers."

Robin and Little John put on women's clothes. Then they stood on the road in their disguises.

"Would you like to know your future?" Robin called to Prince John.

"Perhaps they're robbers," John's friend, Sir Hiss, told him.

"Women aren't robbers. Go away, Hiss!" John answered. He called to Robin, "Come inside! Am I going to be King of England?"

"Close your eyes," Robin said. Prince John closed his eyes. "Yes, you're going to be king," Robin said. "A great king, a handsome king ..."

John smiled. Robin quietly took his bags of money – and his clothes. Then he and Little John ran away.

John opened his eyes. "They robbed me!" he shouted.

Hiss came back. "I told you!" he said.

"Get Robin Hood!" Prince John told the Sheriff of Nottingham angrily.

But Robin did not stop robbing rich people. Poor people had to pay higher and higher taxes, and he wanted to help them. He gave the money to them.

One day, the Sheriff visited a large, poor family and took a young boy's birthday money. The boy was sad.

After the Sheriff left, Robin arrived in disguise.

"Happy birthday, son!" he said, and he took off his disguise. "Here's a present for you."

He gave the boy a bow and arrow, and his hat. He gave the mother some money.

"Don't be sad," he told her. "One day, the people of Nottingham are going to be happy again."

The little boy shot an arrow – into the yard of Prince John's castle. He and his friends went inside. They met Maid Marian and her friend Klucky.

"That's Robin Hood's hat!" Marian said. She looked sad.

"Do you love him?" one of the children asked.

"I do," Marian answered. "But I went away to London. He doesn't remember me now."

In Sherwood Forest, Robin cooked lunch.

"That smells terrible," Little John said. "You're burning it, Robin!"

"I'm sorry," Robin said sadly. "I'm thinking about Marian again. I love her. She also loved me, a long time ago. But now she lives in a castle and I live here."

There is a tournament tomorrow. Robin hopes to see her there.

Robin and Little John went to the tournament in disguise, but Marian knew Robin's eyes. She smiled at him and he gave her a flower.

The tournament began. People shot their first arrows. They shot again and again – and Robin was the best. Prince John looked at him carefully. He had a plan, but Robin did not know that.

In the end, there were only two men in the tournament – Robin and the Sheriff of Nottingham – and Robin won. Then John cut off Robin's disguise and Robin became his prisoner.

"You're going to die!" Prince John shouted.

"No!" Marian cried. "I love him!"

"And I love you," Robin told her. "And King Richard!"

"Hooray for King Richard!" people shouted.

Little John held a knife at Prince John's back.

"The prisoner can go!" the Prince said, afraid.

Marian ran to Robin.

"I can't live without you," she said.

But the Sheriff saw Little John and a fight began.
Little John and Robin fought the Sheriff, the
guards, and Prince John. After Robin
saved Marian, they ran
into the forest.

Robin and Marian walked and talked in Sherwood Forest. Then, in Robin's forest home, they sang and danced with their friends. They laughed about the man who wanted to be king. That night, they forgot their problems.

"He can take our money, but we're going to take it back!" they sang.

In his castle, Prince John was very, very angry.

The poor people of Nottingham had to pay more taxes. They lost their houses because they could not pay. They went to prison. They were all hungry.

At the church, Friar Tuck tried to help the poorest people. But the Sheriff took the church's money, too.

Friar Tuck fought the Sheriff. "Thief!" he cried.

The Sheriff took him to prison.

Prince John had a lot of money, but he did not have Robin Hood.

"I know!" Prince John shouted suddenly. "Friar Tuck is Robin's friend. Let's kill him in the prison yard. Robin can't stay away — and my guards are ready for him."

But Robin, in disguise, learned about the plan.

"We must save Friar Tuck," he told Little John.

That night, there were guards all around the prison, but Robin and Little John found a way past them. The Sheriff was asleep in the yard.

Robin took a guard's uniform and went into the yard in disguise. He opened the prison door. Then he watched the Sheriff, and Little John went inside.

"Save the prisoners!" Robin said quietly.

Robin climbed into the castle. Prince John and Sir Hiss were asleep in their beds with money all around them.

Robin shot an arrow, with a rope, to Little John outside the prison. Then he sent the moneybags down the rope one at a time. After every bag was in the prison yard, he also went down the rope.

Prince John, Hiss, and the Sheriff were awake now, but the prisoners left with the money. Robin helped the last prisoner, a child. The child ran outside, but the door closed in front of Robin.

The guards ran after him, but he climbed up the castle wall and back inside. He fought the sheriff, and the castle caught fire.

Robin ran up the stairs, through the fire, to an open window. Then he jumped into the water below. Prince John's guards shot at him.

Little John watched from the trees. Where was Robin? He waited.

Prince John and Hiss also watched and waited. There was Robin's hat, with an arrow through it! They turned happily away.

Little John cried.

Suddenly, Robin climbed out of the water! Little John was *very* happy to see Robin.

"Look!" Hiss cried to Prince John, from inside the castle. "He got away again!"

"No!" John shouted.

"Your plans never work," Hiss told him, "and your castle is burning to the ground."

John was angry with Hiss and tried to hit him.

Some time later, King Richard came back to England. He sent Prince John, Sir Hiss, and the Sheriff to prison.

Then one fine day, in Friar Tuck's church, Maid Marian became Robin Hood's wife. The people of Nottingham were happy for Robin and Marian – and they had hope for the future.

And that is the end of this story.

Activity page ❶

Before You Read

1 **What do you know about the story of Robin Hood?**

a Who was Robin Hood?

b Where did he live?

c Why did he live there?

d What did he and his friends do?

2 **Look at the picture.**

a What do these words mean?

> tournament   sheriff   guard   bow   arrow   shoot   rope

b Match the names with the pictures a–e. Who are Robin Hood's friends? Who wants to hurt him?

> Friar Tuck   Robin Hood   Maid Marian
> The Sheriff of Nottingham   Little John

Activity page ❷

After You Read

❶ Write short answers to these questions.

  a Was Prince John the King of England?

  b Did Robin Hood and Little John rob Prince John?

  c Could the poor people of Nottingham pay Prince John's taxes?

  d Were Robin Hood and Maid Marian in love?

  e Did Robin Hood win the tournament?

  f Did Prince John put Robin in prison?

  g Did Robin keep Prince John's money?

  h Did the story end happily for Prince John, Hiss, and the Sheriff?

❷ Who is speaking?

  a "This is going to be a good day for the poor people of Nottingham."

  b "Am I going to be King of England?"

  c "One day, the people of Nottingham are going to be happy again."

  d "He doesn't remember me now."

  e "And I love you. And King Richard!"

  f "Thief!"

  g "Save the prisoners!"

  h "Your plans never work, and your castle is burning to the ground."

❸ Finish these sentences.

  a Robin Hood and his friends robbed people because ...

  b They were right to do this because ...

    or

    They were wrong to do this because ...